Cornish Cats

drawn by
Ian Heard

Bossiney Books · Launceston

This reprint 2006
First published 2003 by Bossiney Books Ltd
Langore, Launceston, Cornwall PL15 8LD
www.bossineybooks.co.uk

ISBN 978-1899383-58-0 ISBN 1-899383-58-1
Printed in Great Britain by R Booth, Mabe, Cornwall

Thunder and Lightning

The beast of Bodmin

Oysters are a
well known
aphro-dizzy cat!

The Saffron Cat

Did you just see the saffron cake?
I left it here right on this plate,
Don't mess around or we'll be late,
I'd love a slice of saffron cake.

Have you seen that saffron cat?
He was lurking here, around the back,
There's currant crumbs upon the mat!
Wait till I see that saffron cat.